Fishing For Stars

C000155771

by Niki Davies

edited by Alison Hedger

A delightful Christmas story with six original songs

Suitable for Reception and Key Stage 1
approximate duration 20 minutes

TEACHER'S BOOK
Complete with music, song words and play

SONGS

1. Fishing For Stars
2. Five Little Stars On The Water
3. What An Enormous Star!
4. High On A Hill
5. Plodding Along
6. This Is The Baby Jesus
FINALE Reprise Song 1. Fishing For Stars

A matching tape cassette of the music for rehearsals and performances is available, Order No. GA11089, Side A with vocals included, and side B with vocals omitted.

© Copyright 1999 Golden Apple Productions
A division of Chester Music Limited
8/9 Frith Street, London W1V 5TZ

Order No. GA11088

ISBN 0-7119-7564-7

CAST LIST

Narrator — an adult may be best, or an older child with a strong voice, who is a fluent reader

Luke (*speaks alone*) — wearing pyjamas

*Five small stars
(*the number of stars can be varied*) } in star costumes

The enormous star (*speaks alone*)

*Shepherds — in traditional Biblical clothes

*Three Kings — wearing crowns

Mary, holding the Baby Jesus

Joseph

Optional animals for the stable

Choir of remaining children dressed as the night sky, in dark blue cloth covered with stars

If the number of children taking part is small, they can all form part of the Choir (except Luke), and step out from the choir to perform their parts.

PROPS

A mattress or inflated li-lo with a colourful duvet and pillow case

Fishing net

Three camel hobby-horses

Baby Jesus doll dressed in white shawl

Low chairs, stools or logs for seating inside the stable (*may not be needed*)

*denotes corporate singing

Luke is tucked up in bed fast asleep. His fishing net beside him.

Narrator   This is a story about a little boy called Luke. More than anything in the world, Luke wanted to catch a star. Every night he took his fishing net to bed with him, and every night he dreamt he went to the lake.

Luke gets up and walks with his fishing net to the "lake". Five little stars tip-toe their way onto the stage and Luke pretends to fish throughout the next song.

SONG 1   FISHING FOR STARS

Off for a walk under the moonlight,
    Off for a walk tonight.
Off for a walk under the moonlight,
    Off for a walk tonight.

    Fishing for stars,
    Fishing for stars.
I'm going to catch a star!

sing twice

The five little stars continue to tip-toe.

SONG ONE FISHING FOR STARS

Happily ♩ = 152

Off for a walk under the moon-light, off for a walk to-

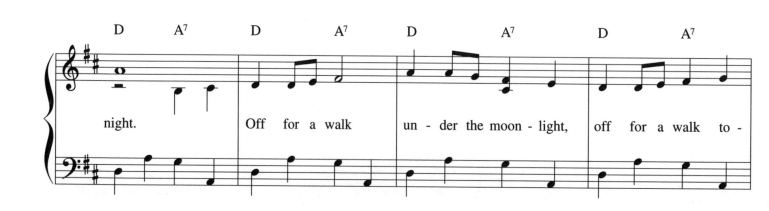

night. Off for a walk under the moon-light, off for a walk to-

night. Fish - ing___ for stars, fish - ing___ for

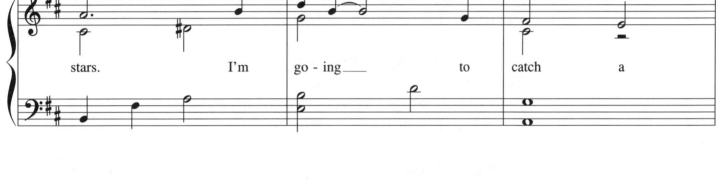

stars. I'm go - ing___ to catch a

star!

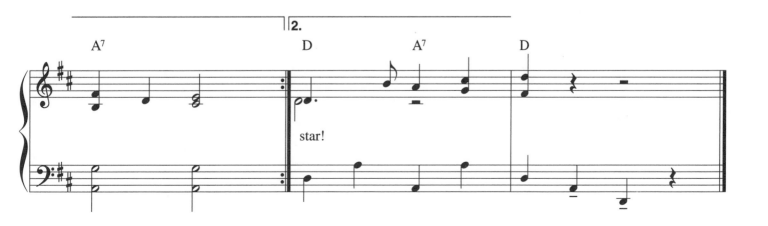

star!

Narrator   Luke sat by the lake and watched the stars dancing on the rippling water. He waited patiently. He tried to catch the stars but they just laughed at him and kept on dancing.

Stars   You can't catch us,
You can't catch us!

SONG 2   FIVE LITTLE STARS ON THE WATER

The little stars continue to dance and run off stage one by one, following the words of the song.

**Five little stars on the water,
Twinkling, laughing at me.
One disappeared in the wink of an eye.
Perhaps it flew back to the sky?**

**Four little stars on the water.
Twinkling, laughing at me.
One disappeared in the wink of an eye.
Perhaps it flew back to the sky?**

Three little stars . . .

Two little stars . . .

**One little star on the water.
Twinkling, laughing at me.
It disappeared in the wink of an eye.
Perhaps it flew back to the sky?**

SONG TWO   FIVE LITTLE STARS ON THE WATER

Five lit - tle stars on the wa - ter,

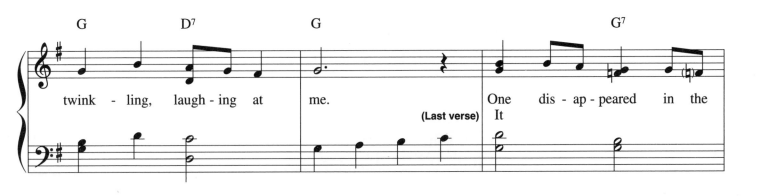

twink - ling, laugh - ing at me.

(Last verse) It

One dis - ap - peared in the

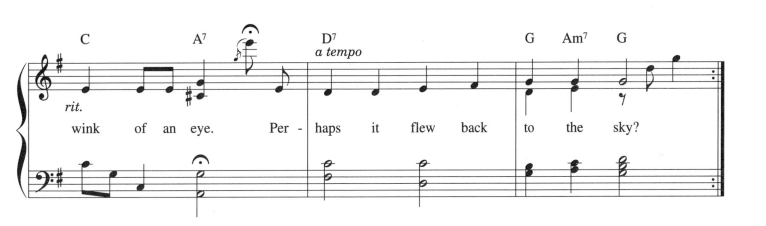

wink of an eye. Per - haps it flew back to the sky?

Narrator   Luke was very disappointed, so he went back to bed.

Luke gets back into bed.

The next night Luke has the same dream.

He gets up and yawns and rubs his eyes as he cannot believe what he sees. An enormous star enters and begins to dance on the "lake".

Tonight an enormous star was dancing on the lake.

During the next song Luke attempts to catch the enormous star in his fishing net.

SONG 3   WHAT AN ENORMOUS STAR!

There is one verse of music before the singing to give an opportunity for the enormous star to dance.

1.   **What an enormous star!**
What a gigantic star you are!
You're shining, shining,
Dancing about on the lake.

2.   **What an enormous star!**
What an amazing star you are!
I'd like to catch you,
Dancing about on the lake.

Repeat 1.   **What an enormous star!**
What a gigantic star you are!
You're shining, shining,
Dancing about on the lake.

SONG THREE WHAT AN ENORMOUS STAR!

Play the music through once before singing to give an opportunity for the enormous star to dance

Coda

Narrator	Then the enormous star shouted out . . .
Star	Hey! I'm not down there. I'm up here. Look up!
Luke	Where?
Star	Here! Catch me if you can!
Narrator	So Luke ran after the star and tried desperately to catch it in his net.

Luke gives chase to the star, as some shepherds enter and sit huddled together on Luke's bed. Luke stops chasing and he and the star stand still and watch the shepherds as they count sheep trying to get to sleep.

SONG 4   HIGH ON A HILL

During the song the shepherds use fingers and toes to count. One could waggle a finger on line four of verse one. By the end of verse three all shepherds are asleep.

1.   **High on a hill, far away
The shepherds count their sheep.
They've just got up to sixty-three.
They're not allowed to cheat!**

2.   **High on a hill, far away
The shepherds count their sheep.
They've just got up to sixty-four.
This counting takes all week!**

3.   **High on a hill, far away
The shepherds count their sheep.
They've just got up to sixty-five,
And now they fall asleep!**

SONG FOUR HIGH ON A HILL

With humour ♩ = 120

Luke walks over to his bed and speaks to the sleeping shepherds.

Luke   Wake up! It's a lovely evening.

Shepherds   Where are you going?

Luke (*pointing*)   To catch that enormous star.

Shepherds   Can we come too?

The shepherds follow Luke in single file

Narrator   So Luke and the shepherds set off together to catch that great big star. They followed it for miles, until they met three very grand-looking people, riding three splendid camels.

Enter the Three Kings on their hobby-horse camels. They take centre stage for the next song, whilst Luke and the shepherds sit on Luke's bed.

SONG 5   PLODDING ALONG

1.   **Three tall camels strolling along
With three Wise Kings upon their backs.
They're plod, plod, plodding,
Plod, plod, plodding.
Plodding along the road.**

2.   **Three Wise Kings with spar-k-ly crowns
Riding camels, tall and proud.
They're plod, plod, plodding,
Plod, plod, plodding.
Plodding along the road.**

Repeat 1.   **Three tall camels strolling along . . .**

SONG FIVE PLODDING ALONG

Happily plodding along! ♩ = 110

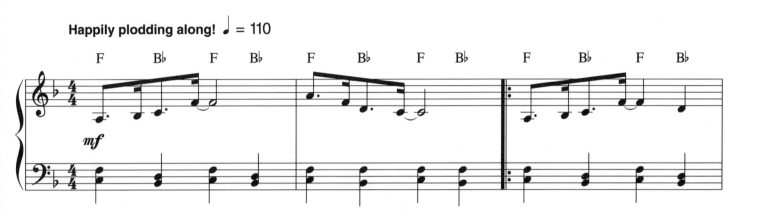

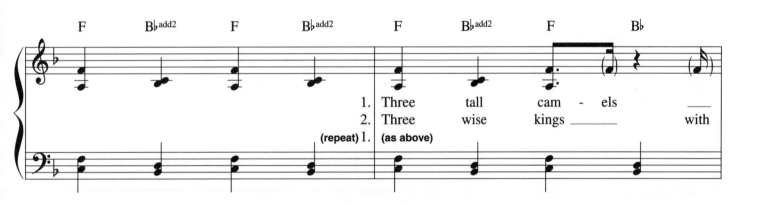

1. Three tall cam - els _____
2. Three wise kings _____ with

(repeat) 1. (as above)

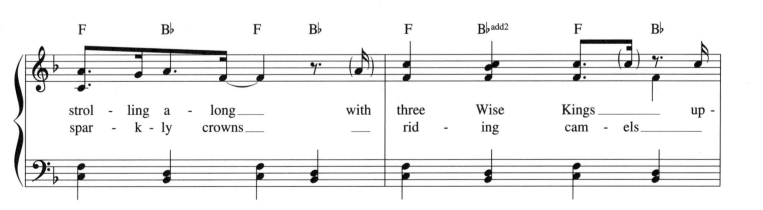

strol - ling a - long____ with three Wise Kings _____ up-
spar - k - ly crowns____ ____ rid - ing cam - els____

13

Kings *(to Luke and Shepherds)*	What have you been doing?
Luke and Shepherds *(pointing and getting up)*	Trying to catch that enormous star.
Kings	Can we come too?

Luke and shepherds form a single file with Luke at the head. The three Kings tag along behind still riding their camels. The enormous star dances and evades being caught in Luke's net. Repeat the music from Song Five for this action.

Narrator	The shepherds and the Three Kings followed Luke for miles. The enormous star led them all the way to Bethlehem. It stopped over a stable.

Enter Joseph and Mary holding the Baby Jesus, followed by the five little stars, and stable animals if any are involved. All stand or sit grouped around Joseph and Mary.

Luke *(to the enormous star)*	Can I catch you now?
Star	No! Look inside that stable!

Luke pretends to open the stable door

Narrator	Luke opened the door of the stable and inside he saw a tiny baby lying in his mother's arms.
Star	This baby is much more special than a star like me! This is the Baby Jesus.

SONG 6   THIS IS THE BABY JESUS

1. **This is the Baby Jesus.**
    Come and see,
    Come and see.
    This is the Baby Jesus,
    Born for you and me.

2. **He is the King of Heaven.**
    Come and see,
    Come and see.
    He is the King of Heaven,
    Born for you and me.

Repeat 1.   **This is the Baby Jesus . . .**

SONG SIX   THIS IS THE BABY JESUS

Narrator   So, one day, if you ever go fishing for stars in your dreams, who knows what you might find!

FINALE   **Reprise Song One FISHING FOR STARS**
(*See pages 4 and 5 for the music*)

Printed in England by Caligraving Limited Thetford Norfolk   8/03 (48379)